BEAU PEEP BOOK 14

From The

DAILY STAR

©1993
Express Newspapers plc
Researched by
Terry Greenwood

Published by

Pedigree BOOKS

Pedigree Books Limited,
The Old Rectory,
Matford Lane, Exeter,
Devon, EX2 4PS.

under licence from
Express Newspapers plc

ISBN 1 874507 120
Printed in Italy

£3.95

BEAU PEEP

EGON

THE NOMAD

MAD PIERRE

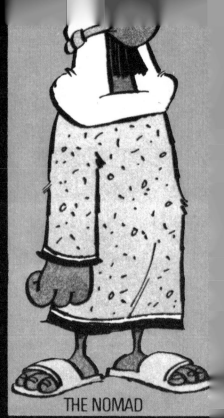

Writer, Roger Kettle (standing) and Artist, Andrew Christine, desperately trying to work out why they've been asked to pose with a cardboard sword.

Photo by Newport Studios, Fife.

THE ADVENTURES OF LEGIONNAIRE BEAU PEEP

FROM THE DAILY STAR

I HEREBY CLAIM THIS LAND!

IT SHALL BE CALLED NOMADIA — LAND OF THE FREE!

VISITORS' PASSPORTS — FIFTY QUID.

3593

WHAT A GREAT IDEA, CREATING MY OWN COUNTRY!

I'M KING, PRIME MINISTER AND POPULATION ALL ROLLED INTO ONE!

MIND YOU, I CAN'T SEE US DOING ALL THAT WELL AT THE OLYMPICS.

3594

IT'S A HARD TASK BEING KING OF MY OWN COUNTRY.

I HAVE TO CREATE LAWS THAT UPHOLD THE TRADITIONS OF JUSTICE.

1A. *Free Beer for the King.*

3595

YOU'RE WRITING YOUR USUAL SENSATIONAL RUBBISH AGAIN!

NO, I'M NOT!

OKAY, WHAT'S YOUR ARTICLE ABOUT CONSERVATION CALLED?

"ALIEN SEX ROMPS CAUSED HOLE IN OZONE LAYER."

3632

THAT REPORTER'S TALKING TO MAD PIERRE.

3633

HE WON'T GET PIERRE TO HELP WITH HIS STUPID ARTICLE ABOUT CONSERVATION!

I'M GETTING A FIVER TO GET PHOTOGRAPHED NAKED AND PAINTED GREEN!

YOU REPORTERS ARE ALL THE SAME!

IT DOESN'T MATTER WHAT WE SAY—YOU JUST WRITE WHAT YOU LIKE!

"I saved Pope from shark attack" claims Legionnaire.

3634

I DON'T WANT TO MAKE THIS PORTRAIT TOO FORMAL.

3650

ARTISTS ALWAYS DO STIFF, BORING PAINTINGS OF MILITARY MEN.

WHAT COLOUR DO YOU WANT THE LOBSTERS?

ALL THE GREAT ARTISTS FIND PAINTING NOSES DIFFICULT.

3651

THE VARIOUS SHADOWS TEND TO DISTORT THE SHAPE.

HOW DO *YOU* COPE?

I DRAW ROUND A BANANA.

WELL, THAT'S YOUR PORTRAIT FINISHED!

3652

REMEMBER I'VE USED ARTISTIC LICENCE — IT'S A LOOSE, MODERN STYLE.

YOU'RE THE THIRD GIRAFFE FROM THE LEFT.

I HATE WRITERS WHO SELL OUT.

THE TYPE WHO MAKE MILLIONS WRITING HORROR STORIES JUST BECAUSE THEY'RE POPULAR.

"The Halloween Nightmare on Chainsaw Street Massacre."

3683

The Halloween Nightmare on Chainsaw Street Massacre.

3684

NO, NO! HOW CAN I WRITE SUCH A STUPID TITLE.

I FORGOT TO MENTION THE ZOMBIE CANNIBALS!

THERE'S A TECHNIQUE IN WRITING HORROR STORIES.

3685

A QUIET START BEFORE YOU HIT THEM WITH THE ACTION.

It was a quiet day. WHUMP! Someone chopped his head off!

LET ME GET THIS RIGHT — TO WIN THE PRIZE...

...I'VE GOT TO KNOCK THE COCONUT OFF BLINDFOLDED USING PING-PONG BALLS?

LEFT HANDED FROM 50 YARDS.

IT'S IMPOSSIBLE TO KNOCK OFF A COCONUT WITH A PING-PONG BALL!

I'D BE AS WELL JUST GIVING YOU THE MONEY AND NOT BOTHERING TO TRY!

OKAY!

I APOLOGIZE FOR CHEATING — I'M ASHAMED OF MYSELF.

I SEEM TO BE OBSESSED WITH MAKING MONEY — BUT I PROMISE I'LL TURN OVER A NEW LEAF.

HERE, THOSE BOOTS MUST BE WORTH A BOB OR TWO!

3569

3570

3571

PEEP IN THE
DAILY STAR
BRITAIN'S BRIGHTEST NEWSPAPER

IT'S HEART-BREAKING WHEN AN EDITOR WON'T PRINT YOUR STORY.

3746

I ONCE HAD AN EXCLUSIVE ABOUT THE ROYAL FAMILY GOING TO A TOP-SECRET MEETING.

I EVEN HAD PICTURES OF THE SPACESHIP!

THE TROUBLE WITH YOU REPORTERS IS THAT YOU TRIVIALISE EVERYTHING.

I SAW THAT PIECE YOU DID ABOUT THE FOREIGN LEGION.

WHAT, THE "WIN A LEGIONNAIRE TO DO YOUR WASHING-UP FOR A MONTH" PIECE?

3747

JOURNALISTS LIKE ME NEVER REST.

EVEN NOW, I'VE GOT TO CHECK A STORY I'VE BEEN WORKING ON.

SO, YOU'VE GOT THAT? IF THE WIFE PHONES, YOU'VE NOT SEEN ME.

3748

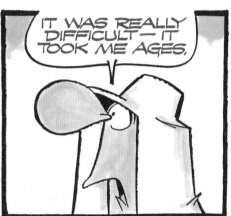

3758

TRY THIS CLUE, DENNIS.

A THREE LETTER WORD, STARTS WITH "C" AND ENDS WITH "T" —DOGS CHASE IT.

A STICK!

GIVE ME ANOTHER— I'M ON A ROLL!

WE ALL HAVE OUR LEVELS IN LIFE, DENNIS.

3759

I ENJOY THE MENTAL STIMULATION OF CRYPTIC CROSSWORDS.

YOU LIKE HICCUPING.

GIVE US ANOTHER CLUE, BEAU!

3760

RIGHT, WHAT'S STUPID, REALLY ANNOYING AND CALLED "DENNIS"?

HOW MANY LETTERS?

HERE COMES "MOUTH."

I WONDER IF HE'S STILL AS RUDE AS HE USED TO BE?

WHAT'S THIS— UGLY NIGHT IN THE PUB?

I'M GOING TO ASK "MOUTH" IF HE WANTS A DRINK.

MAYBE IF WE GET TO KNOW HIM, HE WON'T BE SO RUDE.

NO THANKS— DRINKING WITH FAT BOYS MAKES ME WANT TO THROW UP.

I DON'T KNOW WHAT IT IS ABOUT "MOUTH."

HE JUST CAN'T CAN'T TALK TO ANYONE WITHOUT BEING RUDE.

HEY, BARTENDER, RING THE CATS' HOME— YOU'VE GOT THEIR URINE SAMPLE BY MISTAKE!

DENNIS IS LATE FOR DUTY.

HE'S BEEN A BIT ACCIDENT-PRONE RECENTLY.

I HOPE NOTHING'S HAPP—

HELP ME.

3814

OKAY, DENNIS— WHAT HAPPENED?

3815

EGON BET ME I COULDN'T GET MY HEAD INTO THIS PAN.

I WON.

YOU PUT YOUR HEAD IN A PAN FOR A BET?

3816

THAT'S THE MOST STUPID THING I'VE EVER HEARD!

AND DOUBLE OR QUITS FOR THE JUG.

Dear Lonely Hearts,

Some years ago, I wrote describing the type of woman I'd like to meet.

Am I still barred?

Dear Lonely Hearts,

I would like to join your "Exclusive Cupid Club for the complete romantic,"

but only if there's decent crumpet in it.

LONELY HEARTS QUESTIONNAIRE.

AS BRIEFLY AS POSSIBLE, DESCRIBE THE ATTRIBUTE YOU APPRECIATE MOST IN A WOMAN,

Nudity.

LONELY HEARTS QUESTIONNAIRE.

WHAT WOULD BE YOUR IDEAL ROMANTIC DATE?

Looking at the moonlight through a Duvet.

Here is my application for the "cupid club for the complete romantic."

3824

I enclose a cheque for £10.50p.

P.S. the 50p is a tip— get me one with a big chest.

A REPLY FROM THE "LONELY HEARTS CLUB"

3825

OUR COMPUTER HAS BEEN UNABLE TO FIND YOU A ROMANTIC PARTNER.

NONE OF THE LADIES LISTED HER HOBBY AS "JUICY KISSING."